* No attempt has been made in this Supplement to amend the Index (P(209) to P(226)) of the Sixth Edition.

CONSTITUTION OF COMMITTEE

SHIPS and OFFSHORE INSTALLATIONS COMMITTEE

Constitution as at 14 April 1993.

The President	(*ex officio*)
D M Carlisle CEng FIEE FIMarE	(Chairman)

D St J Seigne CEng FIEE FIMarE
E E Simpson CEng MIEE MIMarE

and	*Nominated by*
T Shore CEng MIEE MIMarE FIQA FInstPet	Association of Electrical Machinery Trades
Appointment pending	Association of Offshore Diving Contractors
R Bond BSc(Eng) CEng MIEE FIMarE Eur Ing M H Mullins BA CEng MIEE FIEIE	BEAMA
C K Reed IEng MIEIE J Ward BA P Waterworth FIEIE	British Cable Makers' Confederation
F Parr IEng MIEIE AMIMarE	British Marine Equipment Council
R L F Smith MA	British Rig Owners' Association
J S Williams BSc CEng MIEE MIMarE	Chamber of Shipping
M S Hunter BSc CEng MIEE MIMarE A G Wood CEng FIMarE	Department of Transport (Marine Directorate)
Appointment pending	EEA
J Osmond AMIMarE	Electrical Contractors' Association

and	*Nominated by*
J F Kerr	Electrical Contractors' Association of Scotland
G Clare FIEE	Engineering Equipment & Materials Users' Association
E J Gorse BA CEng MIEE	Health and Safety Executive (Offshore Safety Division)
H Rush CEng FIMarE MIEIE	Institute of Marine Engineers
S C Williams CEng MIEE MInstPet	Institute of Petroleum
M J Gosling IEng MIEIE	Institution of Electrical & Electronics Incorporated Engineers
G G Reid MSc CEng MIEE	Institution of Engineers & Shipbuilders in Scotland
Eur Ing I F Davies BSc CEng FIEE FInstP	Lighting Industry Federation Ltd.

C Porter CEng FIEE MIMarE FIQA   ⎫ Lloyd's Register of
A Sylvester BSc CEng MIEE   ⎬ Shipping

A Evans   Oil Industry International Exploration & Production Forum

Dr R E Adjaye PhD CEng FIEE   ⎫
Eur Ing G J Stobie BSc CEng   ⎬ UK Offshore Operators'
         MIMechE   ⎭ Association

T R Foster BSc CEng MIEE   ⎫
J D McIver CEng FIEE FIMarE   ⎬ Co-opted
         FRINA   ⎭ Members
A Vickery CEng MIEE

Supplement to the Sixth Edition of the Regulations for the Electrical and Electronic Equipment of Ships with Recommended Practice for their Implementation.

INTRODUCTION

Alterations and additions to Parts 2 and 3 of the Sixth Edition have been approved by the Council of the Institution and are contained in this Supplement. These alterations and additions shall come into effect as from 31 March 1994, the date of issue of this Supplement.

The Sixth Edition of the Regulations for the Electrical and Electronic Equipment of Ships with Recommended Practice for their Implementation, read together with the alterations and additions detailed in this Supplement, shall form the current (revised) Regulations and Recommended Practice for their Implementation and shall remain in force until formally superseded by notice or by the issue of later editions or supplements.

Note: Where cross-references are made in this Supplement to any Clauses, etc., that are, themselves, the subject of a revision, then such cross-references are identified thus "(*)".

Appendix 2 summarises those pages, Clauses and Sub-Clauses of the 1990, Sixth Edition affected by the amendments contained in this Supplement.

ALTERATIONS AND ADDITIONS TO THE SIXTH EDITION

P*(iv)*, add: SIXTH EDITION   Issued in 1990.
                                         Supplement issued, 1994.

P*(xiii)* - P*(xix)*,   PART 2:   replace in total by the revised text given in
                             pages x to xv inclusive.

UNITED KINGDOM STATUTORY REQUIREMENTS AND OTHER RELEVANT GUIDANCE

1   Statutory Requirements

Of the Statutory requirements which apply where a ship is to be registered under the United Kingdom Merchant Shipping Act 1894, the following Statutory Instruments made under that Act and subsequent Merchant Shipping Acts have technical relevance to electrical installations:

Statutory Instrument No:	Title	References of Special Interest
1.1	Construction and equipment	
(1) 1987 No. 1961	Merchant Shipping (Pilot Ladders and Hoists) Regulations 1987	Regulation 9(5)( )
(2) 1984 No. 1216	Merchant Shipping (Passenger Ship Construction and Survey) Regulations 1984	Regulations 42-54 inclusive, 56(4) and (5), 67, 68(9), (10) and (16), 69 (see Note 1)
(3) 1984 No. 1217	Merchant Shipping (Cargo Ship Construction and Survey) Regulations 1984	Regulations 14(4), (5) and (7), 24, 25(9), (10) and (16), 26, 32-41 inclusive, 42-50 inclusive (see Note 2)
(4) 1986 No. 1067	Merchant Shipping (Cargo Ship Construction and Survey) Regulations 1984 (Amendment) Regulations 1986	Regulations (4) and (5)
(5) 1987 No. 549	Merchant Shipping (IBC Code) Regulations 1987	Regulation 3 (see Note 3)
(6) 1986 No. 1073	Merchant Shipping (Gas Carriers) Regulations 1986	Regulation 3 (see Note 3)

(7)	1987 No. 1886	Merchant Shipping (Passenger Ship Construction) (Amendment) Regulations 1987	Regulation 3(3)
(8)	1984 No. 408	Merchant Shipping (Health and Safety General Duties) Regulations 1984	
(9)	1988 No. 1636	Merchant Shipping (Guarding of Machinery and Safety of Electrical Equipment) Regulations 1988	
(10)	1990 No. 892	Merchant Shipping (Passenger Ship Construction and Survey) (Amendment) Regulations 1990	Regulations 15A(8) and (9)
(11)	1992 No. 135	Merchant Shipping (Cargo Ship Construction and Survey) Regulations 1984 (Amendment) Regulations 1992	Regulations 8E (1) and (2)

NOTE 1: The electrical equipment and installation required by Regulation 43 of SI 1984 No. 1216 shall comply with the requirements specified in the current Merchant Shipping Notice relevant to that Regulation.

NOTE 2: The electrical equipment and installations required by Regulation 42 of SI 1984 No. 1217 shall comply with the requirements specified in the current Merchant Shipping Notice relevant to that Regulation.

NOTE 3: Where appropriate, these Regulations require compliance with the following International Maritime Organisation (IMO) publications:

International Code for the Construction and Equipment of Ships Carrying Dangerous Chemicals in Bulk (IBC)	Regulations 3.7.8, 3.7.10, 10.1 to 10.4 inclusive, 15.3.10, 15.11.5 and 15.15

| | International Code for the Construction and Equipment of Ships Carrying Liquefied Gases in Bulk (IGC) | Regulations 1.3, 3.6, 10.1 to 10.2.5.4 inclusive, 12.1.9, 12.1.10 and 17.2 |

1.2 Fire and life-saving

| (1) | 1984 No. 1218 | Merchant Shipping (Fire Protection) Regulations 1984 | Regulations 70(1) and (2), 89, Schedule 7 (6) and (8), Schedule 8(6), Schedule 10(3)(b) (iii) and (3)(c), Schedule 11(1)(b) and (c), (2)(f) and (3)(a), Schedule 12(1)(c) and (d) and (3)(a) |
| (2) | 1986 No. 1066 | Merchant Shipping (Life-Saving Appliances) Regulations 1986 | Regulations 15(4) and (5) and 18(8) |

1.3 Radio and navigational equipment

(1)	1974 No. 1919	Merchant Shipping (Radio) (Fishing Vessels) Rules 1974	Rules 4 and 5
(2)	1992 No. 3	Merchant Shipping (Radio Installations) Regulations 1992	Regulations 14, 22, 27, 33, 41, 45(2) and Schedule 4
(3)	1993 No. 69	Merchant Shipping (Navigational equipment) Regulations 1993	Regulation 5, 6 and 7

1.4   Crew accommodation

1978 No. 795	Merchant Shipping (Crew Accommodation) Regulations 1978	Regulations 7(6), 14 (5), 15(4), (5) and (7), 16(6), 23(2)(c), 23(5)(j), 25(5)(b) and (g), Schedule 3, Schedule 4 paras (7) and (11), Schedule 6 paras 8(5) and (6), Schedule 6 para 9(6) and Appendix 2 para 5

1.5   Fishing vessels

1975 No. 330	Fishing Vessels (Safety Provisions) Rules 1975	Rules 34(3) and (9), 35(3), 38-43 inclusive, 111(4) and 116

1.6   Diving and submersibles

1981 No. 1098	Merchant Shipping (Submersible Craft Construction and Survey) Regulations 1981	Schedule 1(2) and Schedule 2(2)

1.7   Dangerous goods and materials hazardous only in bulk

(1)	1990 No. 2605	Merchant Shipping (Dangerous Goods and Marine Pollutants) Regulations 1990	

(2)   Where appropriate, these Regulations require compliance with:

	(i)	IMO International Maritime Dangerous Goods Code, 1990 Edition (Amdt 26-91)	Vol II Class 1 paragraphs 5.3.5, 5.3.6, 7.1, 7.2 and Appendix 2
	(ii)	IMO Code of Safe Practice for solid cargoes (see also 5.1)	Appendix B
(3)	1984 No. 1218	Merchant Shipping (Fire Protection) Regulations 1984	Regulation 143

1.8   The above Statutory Instruments may be obtained from Her Majesty's Stationery Office (HMSO), 51 Nine Elms Lane, London, United Kingdom, SW8 5DR.

Merchant Shipping Notices may be obtained from the Department of Transport, Marine Library, Spring Place, 105 Commercial Road, Southampton, United Kingdom, SO15 1EG.

The above IMO publications may be obtained from the International Maritime Organisation, 4 Albert Embankment, London, United Kingdom, SE1 7SR.

2.   Where compliance with The Safety of Life at Sea Convention 1974 (SOLAS) as amended and its Protocol of 1978 is required, the provisions of the Convention and its Protocol are embodied, where appropriate, in the Statutory Instruments listed in 1. above.

3.   While work is being carried out in harbour, compliance is required with the Health and Safety at Work etc. Act 1974, and the Electricity at Work Regulations 1989, SI 1989 No. 635.

4.   Instructions for the Guidance of Surveyors

The Instructions should be referred to for the following subjects:

> Survey of Passenger Ships
> Survey of Fire Protection Arrangements in Merchant Ships
> Survey of Life-Saving Appliances
> Survey of Merchant Shipping Radio Installations
> Survey of Merchant Shipping Navigational Equipment Installations
> Survey of Crew Accommodation in Merchant Ships
> Survey of Lights and Signalling Equipment
> Survey of Fishing Vessels
> Survey of Fishing Vessel Radio Installations
> Survey of Submersible Craft
> Survey of Chemical Tankers

Instructions for the Survey of Submersible Craft may be obtained from the Marine Library. All other Instructions may be obtained from HMSO.

5.   Other Relevant Guidance

5.1   Merchant Shipping Notice No. M.971. The safe carriage of coal cargoes. Emission of flammable gases and spontaneous combustion. Obtainable from the Marine Library.

5.2   Merchant Shipping Notice No. M.752. Safety. Electric shock hazard in the use of electric arc welding plant. Obtainable from the Marine Library.

5.3   The Code of Practice for the safe use of electricity underwater (September 1985) published by the Association of Offshore Diving Contractors, 177A High Street, Beckenham, Kent, United Kingdom, BR3 1AH.

5.4   General requirements for marine navigational equipment 1982. Obtainable from HMSO.

5.5   Home Office Code of Practice for ships wire antenna systems for radiotelegraphy transmissions, MPT 1270. Obtainable from HMSO.

5.6   Programmable Electronic Systems in Safety Related Systems, published by the Health and Safety Executive. Obtainable from HMSO.

5.7   Guidelines for the specification and operation of dynamically positioned diving support vessels (May 1983) issued by the Petroleum Engineering Division of the UK Department of Energy and the Norwegian Petroleum Directorate. Obtainable from HMSO.

5.8   Merchant Shipping Notice No. M.1458. Offshore Support Vessels, Paragraph 3.8, Electrical Installations. Obtainable from the Marine Library.

5.9   Guidance Note GS 43 Lithium Batteries, published by the Health and Safety Executive. Obtainable from HMSO.

AMENDMENTS to
PART 3

Section 1

P(5), Clause 1.18; add a second paragraph:

Enclosures having a degree of protection IP22 or better should not have the cable-entry at the top unless the cable-entry plate and/or cable attachments are made so as to exclude water. Enclosures for locations on open deck should have bottom entries unless the cable entry and/or attachments are made so as to exclude water.

P(6), Clause 1.29; add 2 Sub-Clauses:

(1)   Conductors and equipment should be placed at such a distance from each magnetic compass or should be so disposed that the interfering external magnetic field is negligible, *i.e.* total angular deviation is not to exceed 30 minutes when any combination of circuits is switched on and off. See BS MA2, Part 3.

(2)   All current carrying parts and connections should be so constructed and secured as to ensure their continued effectiveness when subjected to vibration. Screws and nuts securing current carrying parts should be effectually locked so that they cannot work loose under vibration.

Section 2

P(9) to P(14); replace completely with the revised text given in pages 4 to 11 inclusive.

SECTION 2

EARTHING AND BONDING

NOTE: The details given in Clauses 2.1 to 2.4 inclusive apply directly to ships with metallic hulls. Additional requirements for ships with non-metallic hulls are detailed in Clause 2.6.

System Earthing

2.1   General

(1)   Earthed neutral or insulated systems are acceptable. For earthed systems in tankers and in other ships of similar hazard, see 23.5(2).

NOTE 1: For further information see Appendix C(*).

NOTE 2: Clause 2.1 should apply to earthed d.c. systems in so far as it is applicable.

(2)   Earthed neutral systems should be so designed that the potential earth fault current:

(i)   will not exceed the design capacity of any part of the systems; and

(ii)   is of sufficient magnitude to operate any protection or indication device.

(3)   The earthing system adopted must take account of, and limit to acceptable values, possible third harmonic circulating currents.

(4)   L.V. earthed neutral systems may be achieved by connecting the neutral point directly to earth. The earth loop impedance should be low enough to permit the passage of a current at least three times the fuse rating for fuse protected circuits or 1.5 times the tripping current of any excess current circuit breaker used to protect the circuit.

4

(5)   H.V. earthed neutral systems should be achieved by inserting impedance in the neutral connection to earth to limit the earth fault current to an acceptable level. The prospective earth fault current should be at least three times the value of current required to operate any earth fault protection devices. In the case of high impedance earthing, the impedance should be such that the earth fault current is slightly higher than the capacitive current of the system. Solid earthing is not recommended for H.V. systems.

(6)   Where an earthed system is divided into two or more sections, means for neutral earthing should be provided for each section.

(7)   All earthing resistors/impedances should be connected to the ship's hull. In addition, earthing resistors/impedances should be bonded together on the hull side of the resistance/impedance. The means of bonding should be separate from that provided at the ship's hull for radio, radar and communications circuits in order to minimise possible interference.

(8)   Efficient means should be provided for detecting defects in the insulation of the system. For systems where the earth fault current exceeds 5 A, automatic tripping devices are to be provided. Where the earth fault current does not exceed 5 A, an indicator may be provided as an alternative to an automatic tripping device. See also 6.11(*).

Earthing of non-current-carrying parts

2.2   General

(1)   Unless specifically included in the exemptions listed in 2.4, all exposed parts and extraneous-conductive-parts should be bonded to the ship's hull. The bonding should be such as to give a substantially equal potential and a sufficiently low earth fault loop impedance to ensure correct operation of protective devices. The bonding should be achieved by means of a separate earth conductor unless the parts under consideration are installed in accordance with 2.2(4).

Extraneous-conductive-parts which are connected to the ship's hull by permanent and reliable metal to metal joints of negligible impedance need not be bonded by separate earthing conductors. Separate supplementary bonding should be provided in situations where this addition is deemed to be necessary.

(2)   Every earthing conductor should be of copper or other corrosion-resistant material and should be securely installed and protected, where necessary, against damage and also, where necessary, against electrolytic corrosion. Connections should be so secured that they cannot work loose under vibration.

(3)   The nominal cross-sectional area of every copper earthing conductor should be not less than that shown in Table 2.2, or Table 2.3, as appropriate. Earthing conductors of materials other than copper should have a resistance not greater than that specified for a copper earthing conductor.

(4)   Metal frames or enclosures of apparatus mounted in direct contact with the ship's hull will normally exhibit a low resistance to earth and no supplementary bonding should be necessary if the supplies to the apparatus and their protection arrangements are in accordance with Table 2.1.

Table 2.1 Conditions for which supplementary bonding is not required

System Voltage 1	Protection arrangements not requiring supplementary bonding 2
110 V up to and including 440 V	Protective device rating 32 A or less; or RCD protected.
55-0-55 V	Fuse rating 16 A or less; or MCB rating 32 A or less; or RCD protected.
24 V	Fuse rating 6 A or less; or MCB rating 10 A or less; or RCD protected.

(5)   Metal parts of portable appliances, other than current- carrying parts and parts exempted in 2.4, should be earthed by means of an earth-continuity conductor in the flexible cable or cord which complies with Table 2.2 and which is earthed, *e.g.* through the associated plug and socket-outlet.

(6)   Every connection to the ship's hull should be made in an accessible position and should be secured by means of a screw or stud of diameter not less than 6 mm which should be used for this purpose only. In all circumstances care should be taken

to ensure bright metallic surfaces at the contact areas immediately before the nut or screw is tightened and, where necessary, to protect the joint with anti-oxidation grease against electrolytic corrosion.

(7)   The earthing of installations in hazardous areas should comply with the requirements of the Appropriate Authority or BS 5345 where appropriate.

2.3   Cables

(1)   The metallic sheaths, armour or braid of cable should be effectively earthed to the ship's hull at both ends, with the following exceptions:

   (i)   Single point earthing may be applied to single core cables for a.c. systems.

   (ii)   In final sub-circuits, earthing may be at the supply end only.

   (iii)   Single point earthing may be applied to control and instrumentation cables, intrinsically safe circuits, control circuits, communications and data transmission circuits, etc., where this is required for technical or security reasons. See also Appendix D(*).

(2)   Earthing may be achieved by means of glands intended for the purpose and so designed as to ensure an effective earth connection. The gland should be firmly attached to, and in effective electrical contact with, a metal frame or enclosure earthed in accordance with these Recommendations.

(3)   Metallic conduit may be earthed by being screwed into a metal enclosure, or by nuts on both sides of the wall of a metal enclosure, provided that surfaces in contact are clean and free from rust, scale and paint, or a serrated washer is used, and that the enclosure is earthed in accordance with these Recommendations. The connection should be painted immediately after assembly in order to inhibit corrosion.

   NOTE: Where metallic conduit is used for earthing purposes it should be screwed into the associated enclosures.

(4)   Alternatively to the methods described in 2.3(2) and 2.3(3), metallic cable sheaths and armour, and conduit, may be earthed by means of clamps or clips of corrosion resistant metal making effective contact with the sheath or armour and earthed metal.

(5)   All joints in metal conduits and ducts and in metal sheaths of cables which are used for earth-continuity should be soundly made and protected, where necessary, against corrosion.

2.4   Exemptions

The following exposed metal parts are exempt from the requirements of 2.2 and 2.3:

(i)   Lamp-caps, where suitably shrouded.

(ii)   Shades, reflectors and guards supported on lampholders or lighting fittings constructed of, or shrouded in, non-conducting material.

(iii)   Metal parts on, or screws in or through, non-conducting materials, which are separated by such material from current-carrying parts and from earthed non-current-carrying parts in such a way that in normal use they cannot become live or come into contact with earthed parts.

(iv)   Portable appliances having "double insulation" (or, in certain circumstances, reinforced insulation) in accordance with a British Standard which has been approved for the purpose.

NOTE: For further information see BS 2754 and Appendix B.

(v)   Bearing housings which are insulated in order to prevent circulation of current in the bearings.

(vi)   Clips for fluorescent lamps.

(vii)   Cable clips.

(viii)   Apparatus supplied at extra-low voltage.

(ix)   Apparatus of "all insulated" construction in which the insulation enclosing the apparatus is durable and substantially continuous.

(x)   Fixed apparatus or parts of apparatus which although not shrouded in insulating material is, nevertheless, so guarded that it cannot be touched and cannot come into contact with exposed metal.

(xi)   Apparatus located in special earth free work rooms.

2.5   Attention is drawn to the earthing requirements covered by 7.13(2), 22.5 and D.4(6)(*).

2.6   Additional requirements for ships with non-metallic hulls

(1)   A main earth conductor bar should be provided at a suitable location, for example, at the main switchboard, to which all non-current-carrying parts not exempted under 2.4 should be connected.

(2)   The main earth conductor bar should be connected to the main earthing plate described in 2.6(3) by a copper conductor having a minimum cross-sectional area of 64 mm^2 preferably of solid strip construction.

(3)   A main earthing plate for communications, lightning and personnel protection should be provided. It should be of not less than 0.25 m^2 in area installed below the light-load waterline so as to remain immersed under all conditions of heel. The earthing plate should be of unpainted copper or other conducting material compatible with sea water and having a surface area sufficient to provide the equivalent low resistance path to earth. Two pillars should be provided, one for connection to the main earth conductor bar and one to the lightning down conductor described in 22.4, made of the same material as the earthing plate and solidly connected to it by welded joints. The establishment of electrochemical corrosion cells with other immersed metallic fittings should be avoided.

(4)   To minimise electromagnetic interference, earthing connections should be run with the associated power cables wherever practical. Three core cable is preferred for lighting circuits.

(5)   Earthing connections of equipment which are sensitive to electromagnetic interference should be made directly to the main earth conductor bar of the main earthing plate.

(6)   The earthing system in accordance with this Section and the lightning protective system in accordance with Section 22 should be run separately down to the pillars at the main earthing plate.

(7)   To dissipate possible charge build up in ships with non-metallic hulls constructed of high resistivity (surface and volume resistivities greater than 10^8 ohms and 10^6 ohms per metre respectively) it is recommended that all metallic objects over 0.6 m in length and over 0.4 m^2 in surface area are earthed.

> NOTE: It may be desirable to bond to the main earth system all metal parts which are in direct contact with the sea, in order to minimise the effects of electrolytic corrosion.

Table 2.2 Size of earth-continuity conductors and earthing connections

Type of earthing connection 1	Cross-sectional area of current-carrying conductor (Note 1) 2	Minimum cross-sectional area of copper earthing connection. 3
(1) Earth-continuity conductor in flexible cable or flexible cord	Not exceeding 16 mm^2	Same as current-carrying conductor.
	Greater than 16 mm^2	Not less than 50% of the cross-sectional area of current-carrying conductor but with a minimum of 16 mm^2.
(2) Insulated earth continuity conductor incorporated in a fixed cable (Note 2)	Not exceeding 16 mm^2	Same as current-carrying conductor but not less than 1.5 mm^2.
	Greater than 16 mm^2	Not less than 50% of the cross-sectional area of current-carrying conductor but with a minimum of 16 mm^2.
(3) Separate fixed conductor Stranded	Not exceeding 3 mm^2	Same as current-carrying conductor but not less than 1.5 mm^2.
Solid	Not exceeding 3 mm^2	3 mm^2
Stranded or Solid	Greater than 3 mm^2 but not exceeding 125 mm^2	Not less than 50% of the cross-sectional area of current-carrying conductor but with a minimum of 3 mm^2.
	Greater than 125 mm^2	64 mm^2

NOTES: 1. The current-carrying conductor is one conductor of a cable or flexible cord.

2. Except for a flat twin-and-earth PVC-insulated cable to BS 6004.

Table 2.3 Size of earth-continuity conductor in flat twin-and-earth PVC-insulated sheathed cables to BS 6004.

Size of current-carrying conductor		Sizes of wires forming earth-continuity conductor	
Nominal cross-sectional area	No. and diameter (mm) of wires	Minimum cross-sectional area	No. and diameter (mm) of wires
1	2	3	4
mm²		mm²	
1.0	1/1.13	1.0	1/1.13
1.5	1/1.38	1.0	1/1.13
2.5	1/1.78	1.5	1/1.38
4	7/0.85	1.5	1/1.38
6	7/1.04	2.5	1/1.78
10	7/1.35	4	7/0.85
16	7/1.70	6	7/1.04

Section 4

P(20), Sub-Clauses 4.6(1) and 4.6(2); replace by:

(1)   Systems having a nominal voltage in excess of 15 kV should be the subject of special consideration and should be to the satisfaction of the Appropriate Authority.

> NOTE: A system operating at over 1 kV should be considered when the use of a lower voltage would result in:

> (i)   a prospective short-circuit current which could occur at any point in the system in service exceeding approximately 70 kA symmetrical; or

> (ii)   the current rating of any generator exceeding approximately 4 kA.

(2)   Nominal system voltages for appliances detailed in Column 1 of Table 4.1 should not exceed the values given in Column 3.

Section 6

P(23), Clause 6.4; replace by:

6.4   Cables for internal wiring should be constructed in accordance with one of the following Standards: BS 6141, BS 6195, BS 6231, BS 6883 or BS 7211. See also 11.17(8)(*).

P(26), Clause 6.11(1); replace "audible or visual" by "audible and visual".

Section 7

P(29), Clause 7.6; replace "lamps" by "luminaires".

P(31), Sub-Clause 7.7(5)(i); replace by:

(i)   In place of the requirements of 7.7(4)(ii) provision should be made in the distribution board to change over the navigation lights to an alternative circuit.

P(32), add Sub-Clause 7.8(7):

(7)   The position of the rudder should be indicated at the principal steering position.

Section 8

P(40), Clause 8.12, line 5; amend "14.13" to "14.12(*)".

P(40), Sub-Clause 8.13(2); replace by:

(2)   Final sub-circuit fuses need not be rated at less than 6 A.

Section 9

P(41), Clause 9.1; replace by:

9.1   Prime movers should conform to the requirements of 1.2, 1.5, 1.10, 1.11, 1.16 and, where applicable, to the relevant parts of Section 25(*). Electrical apparatus provided with these prime movers should conform to the requirements of all relevant Sections of these Recommendations. Guidance on the requirements for prime movers for driving generators may be obtained from the following British Standards where relevant:

     (i)   steam turbines - BS 132, BS 752, BS 5968;

     (ii)   gas turbines - BS 3135, BS 3863;

     (iii)   oil engines - BS 5514.

P(43), Clause 9.10; add the following Sub-Clauses:

(1)   Where motors are to be operated on a non-sinusoidal and/or variable frequency supply, care should be taken to ensure that any additional heating does not impair the service life of the motor.

(2)   Where cooling-water is used, the cooler should be so arranged as to minimise the risk of entry of water into the machine whether by leakage or condensation in the heat exchanger.

P(44), Clause 9.14; add the following Sub-Clauses:

(1)   Generators and motors should be efficiently and continuously lubricated at all running speeds and all normal working bearing temperatures.

(2)   Means should be provided to avoid the lubricant from creeping along the shaft or otherwise gaining access to the insulation of the machine or any live part thereof.

(3)   Measures should be taken if necessary to avoid the circulation of currents between the shaft and bearings.

     NOTE: Circulating currents can cause the deterioration of bearing components and also be a possible ignition source of any explosive gas/air mixture which may be present.

P(44), Clause 9.19, line 2; amend "9.19(1) to 9.19(3)" to "9.19(1) to 9.19(4)(*)". Also add the following Sub-Clause:

(4)   The generating plant should have a transient voltage response such that the anticipated motor starting currents can be accommodated without such voltage drop as would cause maloperation of or damage to other equipment.

Section 10

P(48), Sub-Clause 10.1(4)(ii), last sentence; amend as follows:

The drain wire cross-sectional area should not be less than 0.5 mm^2 and with a minimum of seven wires.

P(48), Sub-Clause 10.1(6); add the following note:

> NOTE: BS 6387 is limited in both the voltage rating and the cable sizes that it covers. Reference should therefore be made to cable manufacturers for guidance on suitable alternative test methods which are no less onerous than those specified in BS 6387.

P(49), Sub-Clause 10.1(7); replace by:

(7)   Non-magnetic materials should be provided for any armouring required for single core cables to be used in a.c. circuits or d.c. circuits having a high ripple current. See also 11.15(*).

P(49), Sub-Clause 10.1(8); replace by:

(8)   The shape of the cable should be such that its entry into an enclosure will not impair the enclosure's specified degree of protection. See also 11.9.

P(49), Clause 10.1; add new Sub-Clause 10.1(9) as follows:

(9)   Where cables are required to operate in areas where contamination by oil is likely to occur the type of oversheath selected should be of an "enhanced oil resistance" grade.

In cases where the contamination is severe the advice of the cable manufacturer should be sought. See the Foreword of BS 6883, also 11.17(14)(*).

P(49), Clause 10.1; add new Sub-Clause 10.1(10) as follows:

(10)   Every core of a single, twin or multicore cable for use as fixed wiring should be identifiable at its terminations and, preferably, throughout its length.

P(49), Clause 10.2; change title of BS 6883 to:

Specification for elastomer insulated cables for fixed wiring in ships and on mobile and fixed offshore units.

Also add: BS 7211 Thermosetting insulated cables (non-armoured) for electric power and lighting with low emission of smoke and corrosive gases when affected by fire.

P(50), Clause 10.2; delete: "(This publication also covers 0.6/1kV cables)". Also add, under the remaining details for IEC 502:

NOTE: IEC 502 also covers 0.6/1 kV cables.

P(50), Clause 10.3; change title of BS 6883 to:

Specification for elastomer insulated cables for fixed wiring in ships and on mobile and fixed offshore units.

Also delete: "(limited to 8 700/15 000 volts)" from the titles of BS 6622 and IEC 502.

Also add a note below the entry for IEC 502 to read:

NOTE: Application of BS 6622 and IEC 502 is limited to 8 700/15 000 V.

P(50), Clause 10.5; add another sentence:

Reference should be made to the manufacturer for details of the actual materials used in a particular cable.

P(51), Table 10.1; replace completely with the revised Table on page 18.

Table 10.1 Guide to types of materials used in cable construction

Type of material 1	Temperature Classification 2
Thermoplastic Insulations	
Polyethylene BS 6234	
Type 03	60 °C
PVC BS 6746	
Type TI 1 General Purpose	70 °C
Type TI 2 Flexible	70 °C
Type TI 4 Installation at Low Temperature	70 °C
Type 4 Flexible	85 °C
Type 5 Hard	85 °C
PVC IEC 92-351	
Type PVC/A	60 °C
Thermoplastic sheaths	
Polyethylene BS 6234	
Type 03C	60 °C
PVC BS 6746	
Type TM1 Hard	70 °C
Type TM2 General Purpose Flexible	70 °C
Type 4 Flexible	85 °C
Type 5 Hard	85 °C
Type 6 General Purpose	70 °C
Type 7 For RF Cables to BS 2316	70 °C
Type 8 For RF Cables to BS 2316	70 °C
Type 9 For Cables with maximum conductor temperature of	90 °C
PVC IEC 92-359	
Type ST1	60 °C
Type ST2	85 °C
Thermosetting Insulations (Rubbers Including Elastomerics)	
BS 6899	
Type GP1 Typically EPR or EPDM for 600/1000V operation	85 °C

Type of material 1	Temperature Classification 2
BS 6899 con'd	
Type GP2 Typically EPR or EPDM for higher voltages	85 °C
Type GP4 Typically EPR or EPDM for 600/1000V operation	90 °C
Type GP5 Typically EPR or EPDM for higher voltages	90 °C
Type GP8 XLPE	90 °C
Type E12 Silicone rubber	150 °C
IEC 92-351	
EPR	85 °C
XLPE	85 °C
S95 Silicone rubber	95 °C
Thermosetting sheath	
BS 6899	
Type RS3 Typically ordinary duty CSP or CPE (GP HOFR)	85 °C
Type RS4 Typically heavy duty CSP or CPE (HD HOFR)	85 °C
BS 6883	
Type A RS3 with enhanced oil resistance typically modified CSP or CPE (GP HOFR)	85 °C*
Type B RS3 with a range of enhanced properties including reduced halogen acid gas emissions, typically a modified CSP or CPE (GP HOFR)	85 °C*
Type C RS3 with a range of enhanced properties specifically low smoke and negligible halogen acid gas emission, typically EVA or EMA	85 °C*
Type D RS3 with a broader range of enhanced properties, oil resistance, low smoke, negligible halogen acid gas emission, typically EVA or EMA	85 °C*
IEC 92-359	
Type SE1 Typically PCP	85 °C
Type SH1 Typically CSP or CPE	85 °C

Section 11

P(52), Clause 11.1, last sentence; amend as follows:

Where it is necessary to use single core cables in a.c. circuits or in d.c. circuits having a high ripple current, special precautions may be required; see 11.15(*).

P(52), Sub-Clause 11.2(1); replace by:

(1)   The voltage rating of any cable should not be less than the nominal voltage of the circuit for which it is used. See the Appendix to this Section for detailed guidance.

P(62), Sub-Clause 11.12(1); add the following note:

NOTE: BS 7609 gives guidance in the installation and inspection of compression type connectors.

P(62), Sub-Clause 11.12(5); replace by:

(5)   At the ends of cables, the insulation should not be removed farther than is necessary having regard to the type of termination used. For cables rated up to 1 kV a.c., the braid, metal sheath, or other covering over the insulation including the tape (if any) in contact therewith, should be cut back at least 13 mm from the end of the insulation in cables up to 13 mm diameter (measured over the insulation) and at least 25 mm from the end of the insulation in cables of greater diameter. For cables rated above 1 kV a.c., the minimum creepage distances given in 24.4 should be complied with. The covering over the insulation should not be cut back beyond the point of entry to the terminal box or fitting.

NOTE: The dimensions referred to above do not apply to mineral-insulated metal sheathed cables.

P(64), Clause 11.15; change heading to:

Installation of single core cables for a.c. distribution and for d.c. distribution of systems with high ripple current.

Also add a new Sub-Clause:

(7)   11.15(1) to 11.15(6) inclusive are generally applicable for d.c. installations in which currents with a high ripple content are present. See also 1.4.

P(65), Sub-Clause 11.17(4); replace by:

(4)   In general, the cables specified in 10.2(*) and 10.3(*) are designed to be suitable for low temperature operating conditions with the exception that the ambient temperature should be above 0°C when installing PVC-insulated or PVC-sheathed cable constructed from PVC compounds given in BS 5467, BS 6346 and IEC 502.

Cables manufactured in accordance with the IEC 92-Series may have an outer sheath of a special PVC with superior low temperature properties to those referred to in BS 5467, BS 6346 and IEC 502, and these cables may be installed at temperatures as low as -10°C.

When agreed between the purchaser and manufacturer, special low temperature grades of PVC can be supplied against the applicable cable standard, for example, BS 6746, Type T14 insulation, which is designed for installation and service at temperatures of -25°C, when used with an appropriate sheathing compound of at least equivalent low temperature performance.

P(65), Sub-Clause 11.17(5); replace by:

(5)   Cables for service in ambient temperatures lower than -30°C should be suitable for the environment and be able to withstand vibration at these low temperatures.

P(66), Sub-Clauses 11.17(8) and 11.17(9); replace by:

(8)   Cables for the internal wiring of switchgear should comply with BS 6141, BS 6195, BS 6231, BS 6883 or BS 7211. The insulation of internal wiring in main control gear and switch-boards should be of a flame-retardant type. When selecting cables for use as internal wiring of equipment, consideration should be given to the products of combustion evolved should the cable be affected by fire.

(9)   Cables for use in radio communication systems and at radio frequencies should comply with BS 2316 and should be installed in compliance with D.4(*).

P(66); add new Sub-Clauses 11.17(13) and 11.17(14) as follows:

(13)   Cables for data transfer and communications should be designed to suit the specified conditions and service.

(14)   Cables for installation where oil or other harmful liquids are present should be selected after consideration of the duty and the environment in which they are to operate.

> NOTE: BS 6883 contains a reference to cables having enhanced oil resistant sheaths as an option; attention is drawn to the Foreword of that Standard.

P(66): add the following new Appendix given on pages 22 and 23 inclusive.

APPENDIX TO SECTION 11

RECOMMENDATIONS FOR THE SELECTION OF CABLES

Voltage Rating

The selection of standard cables of appropriate voltage designations for particular systems depends on the system voltage and the system earthing arrangements. To facilitate the selection of the cable, systems are divided into the following three Categories:

(a)   Category A. This category comprises those systems in which any phase conductor that comes into contact with earth or an earthed conductor is automatically disconnected from the system.

(b)   Category B. This category comprises those systems that, under fault conditions, are operated for a short time, not exceeding 8 hours on any occasion, with one phase earthed.

NOTE: In a system where an earth fault is not automatically and promptly eliminated, the increased stresses on the insulation of cables during the earth fault are likely to affect the life of the cables to a certain degree. If the system is expected to be operated fairly often with a sustained earth fault, it may be preferable to use cables suitable for Category C. In any case, for classification as Category B, the expected total duration of earth faults in any year should not exceed 125 hours.

(c)   Category C. This category comprises all systems that do not fall into Categories A or B.

Table 11.4 gives the lowest rated voltage of cable which should be used for an a.c. system according to the voltage and Category of the system.

The nominal system voltage, U, given in the Table is the power frequency voltage between phase conductors. U_o is the power frequency voltage to earth for which the cable is designed.

The maximum system voltage, U_m, is the highest power frequency voltage between phase conductors which may be sustained under normal operating conditions at any time and at any point in the system. It excludes transient voltage conditions and rapid disconnection of loads.

The nominal system voltages from 3.3 kV to 15 kV shown in Table 11.4 are generally in accordance with Series 1 in IEC 38. For nominal system voltages between these standard voltages, and also between 1 kV and 3.3 kV, the cables should be selected with a rated voltage not less than the next higher standard value. For example, for a 13.8 kV system of Category A or B, the cable should have a rated voltage not less than 8.7/15 kV.

The 600/1000 V cables may be used for d.c. systems up to 1500 V and the 1900/3300 V cables for d.c. systems up to 3000 V to earth. However, consideration should be given to the peak value when determining the voltage of d.c. systems derived from rectifiers, bearing in mind that smoothing does not modify the peak value when the semiconductors are operating on an open circuit.

Table 11.4 Selection of cables for a.c. systems

System voltage		System Category	Minimum rated voltage of cable U_o/U	
Nominal voltage U	Maximum sustained voltage, Um		Unscreened	Single-core or screened
1	2	3	4	5
kV	kV		kV	kV
up to 0.25	0.28	A, B or C	0.15 / 0.25	-
1.0	1.1	A, B or C	0.6 / 1	0.6 / 1
3.3	3.6	A or B	1.9 / 3.3	1.9 / 3.3
3.3	3.6	C	3.3 / 3.3	3.8 / 6.6
6.6	7.2	A or B	3.8 / 6.6	3.8 / 6.6
6.6	7.2	C	6.6 / 6.6	6.35 / 11
11	12.0	A or B	6.35 / 11	6.35 / 11
11	12.0	C	-	8.7 / 15
15	17.5	A or B	-	8.7 / 15

Section 13

P(88), Clause 13.1; add the following note:

NOTE: BS 587 is obsolescent.

P(90), Clause 13.10, last sentence; amend as follows:

Double brush-contacts should, preferably, be fitted to provide a positive contact.

Section 14

P(91) to P(96); replace completely with the revised text given in pages 25 to 34 inclusive.

SECTION 14

BATTERIES

General

14.1 This Section relates principally to secondary batteries of the vented, sealed and valve regulated sealed types which are installed permanently in position. Safety recommendations concerning primary cells are included in 14.14.

14.2 Battery types

(1) A vented battery is one in which the products of electrolysis are freely released whilst operating on charge, overcharge and discharge and which can be replaced.

(2) A sealed battery is made up of primary cells or secondary cells in which the products of electrolysis are reconstituted within each individual gas-tight cell or unit. The electrolyte cannot be replaced and the battery is capable of operating on charge, overcharge and discharge without releasing gas under normal conditions, but allows the escape of gas if the internal pressure exceeds a critical value.

(3) A valve regulated sealed battery is a unit in which the majority of the products of electrolysis are reconstituted within each individual cell or unit. The electrolyte cannot be replaced and the battery is capable of operating on charge, overcharge and discharge under normal conditions with minimal release of gas by a pressure relief valve.

NOTE 1: The current British and International Standards predate the above definitions and normally only the very small button type batteries, such as are
commonly used in portable equipment, will comply with the definitions in
14.2(2).

NOTE 2: Care should be taken when replacing cells in portable apparatus certified
for use in hazardous areas. Only the type of cell certified with the apparatus
should be used. An incorrect type, such as the so called "high power" types,

could lead to excessive temperatures under certain fault conditions. Not only could this lead to incendive conditions but it could also present a burn hazard to personnel.

14.3   Each battery should be provided with a durable name plate securely attached or, alternatively, fitted adjacent to the battery, bearing the maker's name and type designation, the ampere-hour rating at some specific rate of discharge (preferably that corresponding to the duty for the specific application) and, for lead-acid batteries, the specific gravity of the electrolyte when the battery is fully charged.

14.4   The batteries should be arranged to facilitate ease of installation, replacement and, where necessary, maintenance. Each cell or crate of cells should be accessible from the top and at least one side.

14.5   The battery may consist of single cells assembled in crates or trays or upon a stand or stands of wood or other suitable material. Crates or trays should be provided with means to facilitate handling and should preferably not exceed 100 kg in weight; individual cells should not exceed 25 kg in weight. Where metal stands are used, non-absorbent insulation appropriate to the working voltage should be provided between the cells and stands. Similar insulating materials should be employed to restrict movement of the cells which would otherwise arise due to movement of the ship. In addition, metallic stands should be insulated from the structure where the battery has a nominal working voltage exceeding 120 V.

14.6   All fittings should be non-corrodible or should be treated with electrolyte-resistant material.

14.7   Batteries should not be installed in sleeping quarters. Batteries should be located where they are not exposed to excessive heat, extreme cold, spray or other conditions which would impair performance or accelerate deterioration.

NOTE: The best operating conditions for a battery are obtained when the ambient temperature is within the range 15°C to 25°C. Attention is drawn to the effect of higher temperatures upon battery performance and to the ambient conditions described in 1.10 against which battery systems should be designed.

Vented Type Batteries

14.8   Construction

The cells of all batteries should be so constructed as to prevent spilling of the electrolyte as a consequence of an inclination of 40 degrees from normal during handling. The plates should be so arranged that they are firmly secured against motion within the containers and should be designed for the least practical shedding of active material. The design should also minimise the emission of electrolyte spray.

14.9   Installation

(1)   Where acid is used as the electrolyte, a tray of lead or wood lined with lead or other electrolyte resisting material should be provided below the cells to contain any leaking electrolyte. The lining should be watertight and carried up to a height of not less than 75 mm on all sides. If of lead, the lining should be 1.5 mm minimum thickness.

(2)   Alternatively, the deck below the cells should be protected with lead or other acid resisting materials to minimise risk of any acid lodging in contact with the structure of the ship. The lining should span the entire floor and be carried up to not less than 150 mm on all sides.

(3)   For alkaline batteries similar arrangements should be adopted using a lining of electrolyte resisting material. If the lining is of steel , it should be not less than 0.8 mm thickness. Deck boxes should be lined to a depth of 75 mm consistent with the methods described above. The interiors of all battery compartments including crates, trays, boxes, shelves and other structural parts therein should be painted with corrosion-resistant paint.

Materials used for coating and lining should not be likely to emit vapours detrimental to the batteries.

(4)   A permanent notice should be exhibited prohibiting naked lights and smoking in battery compartments.

14.10   Location

(1)   Batteries connected to a charging device with a power output of more than 2 kW (calculated from the maximum obtainable charging current and the nominal

voltage of the battery) should be installed in a compartment assigned to batteries only, but may be installed in a suitable box on deck. See also 14.7.

(2)   Batteries connected to a charging device with a power output within the range of 0.2 kW to 2 kW (calculated as under 14.10(1)) may be installed in accordance with one of the following alternatives:

    (i)   in a battery compartment or room; or

    (ii)   in a box on deck; or

    (iii)   in a box in a machinery or similar space.

(3)   Batteries connected to a charging device with a power output of less than 0.2 kW (calculated as under 14.10(1)) may be installed in accordance with one of the following alternatives:

    (i)   open, if protected from falling objects; or

    (ii)   in a battery box in any suitable space.

(4)   Batteries should be so located that adjacent equipment is not rendered inoperative by corrosion from battery emissions.

(5)   Starter batteries should be located as close as practicable to the engine or engines served, to limit voltage drop in cables at the high current required.

(6)   No battery compartment should form a means of access to any other compartment.

(7)   Where lead acid and alkaline batteries are installed, precautions should be taken to prevent possible contamination of the electrolytes. If the same compartment is used for both battery types, separation should be provided by screens.

    NOTE: Separate tools such as hydrometers, topping-up devices, etc., should be provided.

(8)   Battery compartments should have gas-tight boundaries where they adjoin accommodation or service spaces, and it is preferable that they should be arranged with access from the open deck.

14.11   Ventilation

(1)   All rooms, compartments and boxes for storage batteries should be arranged and/or ventilated to avoid accumulation of flammable gas. Particular attention should be given to the fact that the gas evolved is lighter than air and will tend to accumulate in any pockets at the top of the available space. Where batteries are arranged in two or more tiers, all shelves except the lowest should have not less than 50 mm space front and back for circulation of air.

(2)   Natural ventilation for battery compartments may be employed if ducts can be run directly from the top of the compartment to the open air above, with no part of the duct more than 45° from the vertical. These ducts should not contain appliances, *e.g.* a flame-barrier, which may impede the free passage of air or gas mixtures. If natural ventilation is impracticable or insufficient, mechanical exhaust ventilation should be provided with the exhaust at the top of the compartment. Adequate openings for inlet air, whether connected to ducts or not, should be provided near the floor of battery compartments or boxes.

(3)   The ventilation system for battery boxes and compartments should be separate from other ventilation systems and the ducts should lead to a location in the open air where any gases can be safely diluted. The location should be away from possible sources of ignition and openings to spaces in which gases might accumulate.

(4)   In every case the ventilation arrangements should be such that the quantity of air expelled is at least equal to:

$$Q = 110 \times I \times n$$

where   Q = Quantity of air expelled in litres per hour.

I = The maximum current delivered by the charging equipment during gas formation, but not less than $\frac{1}{4}$ of the maximum obtainable charging current in amperes.

n = Number of cells in series.

(5)   Batteries in rooms, compartments or boxes connected to a charging device with a total maximum power output of more than 2 kW should be ventilated by mechanical exhaust.

(6)   Where lockers or boxes are provided for batteries in machinery spaces and other well-ventilated compartments, the duct should terminate not less than 900 mm above the battery enclosure.

(7)   Boxes for batteries should have, for ventilation, openings near the top to permit escape of gas. Holes for air inlet should be provided on opposite sides of the box as a minimum. The entire box, including openings for ventilation, should be sufficiently weatherproof to prevent entrance of spray or rain.

(8)   Ventilating fans for battery compartments should be so constructed and be of material such as to minimise risk of sparking in the event of the impeller touching the casing. Impellers of non-metallic material should be such that sparking due to static discharge is minimised.

(9)   Ducts should be made of a corrosion-resisting material or their interior surfaces should be painted with electrolyte resistant paint.

(10)   Any fan motor associated with a duct used to exhaust air from a battery compartment should be placed external to the duct and the compartment.

(11)   All openings through battery compartment bulkheads or decks, other than ventilation openings, should be effectively sealed to reduce the possibility of escape of gas from the battery compartment.

14.12   Electrical installations in battery compartments and rooms

(1)   Switches, fuses and other electrical equipment likely to cause an arc should not be placed within the battery compartment.

(2)   Luminaires should be permanently wired and fitted outside the space so that the space is illuminated through permanently fixed lenses or ports fitted in the bulkhead or deck, so arranged to maintain the gas-tight integrity of the compartment. Alternatively, luminaires of the type certified for use in hydrogen atmospheres may be used within the battery compartment.

(3)   Cables should not normally be installed in battery compartments unless they form part of intrinsically safe circuits or are serving permitted equipment within the compartment. Through-runs of cables may be permitted within the compartment where installation elsewhere is impracticable when they should either:

(i)   be in seamless steel conduit or equivalent, without joints or junction boxes, which is gas-tight to the battery compartment; or

(ii)   include a metallic sheath or braid or wire armour with an electrolyte resisting impervious non-metallic sheath applied over the metallic covering.

(4)   Cable penetration arrangements should maintain the gas-tight integrity of the battery compartment.

(5)   In some circumstances it may be impracticable to provide overload and short-circuit protection for cables connected to batteries, *e.g.* within battery compartments and in engine starting circuits. Unprotected cable runs should be kept as short as possible and special precautions should be taken to minimise the risk of faults, *e.g.* single core with additional sleeves over the insulation of each core, with shrouded terminals.

Sealed Batteries

14.13   Special ventilation arrangements to avoid the accumulation of flammable gases are not normally necessary for batteries in accordance with 14.2(2), provided that precautions are taken to minimise the risk of cell abuse. Causes of cell abuse include:

(i)   attempts to charge primary cells, mixing used and unused cells, mixing cells of different electrochemical systems, reversing one cell in a set of three or more and the use of any alternative power source provided for the equipment.

(ii)   short-circuits, which can occur due to poor insulation of the cell enclosure, water ingress into the cell enclosure and unsuitable storage of cells.

NOTE: For batteries in portable apparatus used in hazardous areas, see 14.2, Note 2.

14.14   Guidance on the use of lithium batteries issued by the Health and Safety Executive should be adhered to, see Part 2, 5.9(*).

Valve Regulated Sealed Batteries

14.15   Valve regulated sealed lead-acid batteries should comply with the requirements of BS 6290, Part 4 and BS 6745, Part 1 and nickel-cadmium to BS 5932 and BS 6115.

Where other Standards are used, precautions to minimise risk due to released gas under normal conditions and risk due to disruption with explosive force in abnormal conditions should be included, see 14.2.

14.16

(1)   The ventilation arrangements of compartments containing valve regulated sealed batteries, as defined in 14.2(3), should comply with 14.11(1) and 14.11(2). These arrangements should be such that the quantity of air expelled is at least equal to:

$$Q = 11 \times I \times n$$

where   Q = Quantity of air expelled in litres per hour.

I = The maximum current delivered by the charging equipment during gas formation, but not less than $\frac{1}{4}$ of the maximum obtainable charging current in amperes.

n = Number of cells in series.

(2)   Compartments containing valve regulated sealed batteries may contain:

(i)   batteries which are of the lead acid or nickel cadmium type provided that precautions are taken to minimise the risk of the charging facilities being connected to the incorrect battery;

(ii)   standard marine electrical equipment, as appropriate.

NOTE: When vented type batteries are located in the same compartment as valve regulated sealed batteries the requirements of 14.11(4) and 14.12 apply.

14.17   Boxes or lockers containing valve regulated sealed batteries should comply with 14.11(7).

Charging Facilities

14.18   For floating service or any other conditions where the load is connected to the battery whilst it is on charge, the maximum battery voltage should not exceed the safe value for any connected apparatus. The voltage characteristics of the generators or rectifiers which will operate in parallel with the batteries should be suitable for each application.

14.19   Where apparatus capable of operation at the maximum charging potential is not available, a voltage regulator or other means of voltage control should be provided.

14.20   Where valve regulated sealed batteries are installed in accordance with 14.16 and 14.19, a device independent of the normal charging arrangements should be provided to prevent gas evolution in excess of the manufacturer's design quantity.

14.21   A suitable warning plate should be fitted to the charger stating:

"Switch off charger before working on battery connections".

14.22   Where a low voltage battery is floated on the line with a resistor in series, all connected apparatus should be capable of withstanding the line voltage to earth. A suitable warning plate should be fitted stating:

"Disconnect charging circuit before working on any circuit connected
to the battery".

14.23   For an emergency supply battery, the arrangements for automatic transfer switching should be such that the emergency supply is available whether the battery is on charge or not.

14.24

(1)   Except as provided by 14.24(2), the charging facilities for any battery should be such that the completely discharged battery can be completely charged in a reasonable time having regard to the service requirements.

(2)   Extra-low voltage batteries provided in duplicate for communication supply (one in service, the other on charge) should be charged at a rate commensurate with the average discharge rate.

14.25   For lead acid batteries which normally stand idle for long periods, trickle charging should be provided to prevent permanent damage due to sulphation on self-discharge.

14.26   Suitable means, including an ammeter and a voltmeter, should be provided for monitoring and controlling the re-charging of each battery, and to protect against discharge of the battery into the charging circuits.

Section 15

P(97), Clause 15.1, first sentence; amend as follows:

Lamps should conform, as regards the type of lamp-cap, mechanical qualities and insulation resistance, to the requirements of BS 161, BS 1075, BS 1853, BS 3677, BS 3767, BS 5971, BS 6193, BS 6982, BS EN 60968, BS EN 60969, or other appropriate British Standard, except that lamps of 150 watts and over should be fitted with Medium Edison Screw (E 27) or Goliath Edison Screw (E 40) caps as appropriate.

P(97), Sub-Clause 15.2(1); add a second sentence:

Lampholders should comply with the requirements of BS 5042 (or IEC 1184), BS 6776 or other appropriate British Standard.

P(98), Sub-Clause 15.2(5), first sentence; amend as follows:

Moulded insulated bayonet-type (B 22) lampholders should be of a T2 temperature rating, see BS 5042 or IEC 1184.

P(98), Table 15.2: amend last entry to Goliath Edison Screw (E40).

P(98), Clause 15.3, second line; amend BS 6702 to BS EN 60400.

P(100), Clause 15.15, first sentence; amend as follows:

Every lamp auxiliary, *i.e.* ballast, inductor, capacitor, starting device and glow starter, should conform to the requirements of:

BS 3772, BS EN 60920, BS EN 60921, BS EN 60922,
BS EN 60923, BS EN 60924, BS EN 60925, BS EN 60926,
BS EN 60927, BS EN 60928, BS EN 60929, BS EN 61046,
BS EN 61047, BS EN 61048, BS EN 61049, or other
appropriate British Standard.

P(100), Clause 15.16, last line; amend as follows:

Lamps and lamp auxiliaries intended to operate on frequencies other than 50 Hz or 60 Hz or from d.c. supplies should achieve similar safety and, where possible, performance requirements as specified in all the appropriate British Standards - see 15.15(*) and Appendix A (*).

P(101), Clause 15.18, first sentence; amend as follows:

Discharge lighting installations using voltages exceeding 650 V r.m.s. measured on open circuit, should comply with BS 559 and BS EN 61050.

Section 16

P(102), Clause 16.1; replace by:

16.1 Electric heating and cooking appliances should comply with the relevant requirements of BS 3456, BS 4167 and BS 5784.

P (102), Clause 16.9, first sentence; amend as follows:

Cooking and heating appliances and their control equipment fitted in galley spaces should have splashproof enclosures (see Table 1.1).

Section 19

P(110), Sub-Clause 19.3(3), second sentence; amend as follows:

This requirement does not apply to insulating cords of cord operated switches.

P(111), Sub-Clauses 19.4(10) and 19.4(11); replace by:

(10)   In washplaces and in spaces containing a fixed bath or shower, with the exception of a connection reserved solely for the use of electric shavers, there should be no socket-outlets and there should be no provision for connecting other portable appliances.

The connection for the electric shaver should only be by means of a shaver supply unit complying with BS 3535 or such a unit combined in a luminaire.

(11)   When installed in other locations, connections for the use of electric shavers should, in addition to complying with 19.4(10)(*), be provided with a suitable current-limiting device and be clearly marked or labelled with the words:

"For shavers only".

Section 20

P(113), Clause 20.2; add the sentence:

Electronic equipment should comply with the safety requirements of BS 415, where applicable.

Section 21

P(115), Sub-Clause 21.2(3); replace the first paragraph by:

The design of the control systems should be such that any failure within them will lead to the least dangerous condition of the controlled process. Such failure should not render any reserve automatic or manual control inoperative. For example, where remote control is provided for safety related or emergency services, local control should be unaffected by a fault, including a cable fault, when local control is selected. See also 1.5.

Where changeover facilities which affect the operation of emergency services are provided, *e.g.* battery isolating switch, the arrangements should be such as to minimize the risk of devices being left in a position which would prevent the emergency services being supplied when required, *e.g.* locking facilities.

Section 23

P(128), Sub-Clause 23.2(1)(i); replace by:

(i)   Electrical equipment is installed and maintained in accordance with BS 5345, where appropriate, and with the exceptions referred to in this Section.

P(139) and P(141), Table 23.2 (part);

transfer item D(iii), with amended "shading", to become item E(iv) and relabel the present D(iv) to become D(iii) and the present E(iv) to become E(v). See pages 39 and 40 for those pages of Table 23.2 that have changed.

Table 23.2 cont. (Modified P (139))

Hazard Category	Description of Location	Typical Example	Permitted Certified Safe type Equipment/Cables
D	(i) Enclosed and semi-enclosed spaces separated by a single bulk-head from cargo/storage tanks and which have continuous mechanical ventilation, except when the ship is in a gas free condition, and loss of ventilation is alarmed at a manned station. e.g.: Pump rooms of storage barges. Pump rooms of oil recovery ships. Spaces separated by a single bulkhead from tanks of recovered oil on oil recovery ships. (ii) Enclosed and semi-enclosed spaces with closed process plant and associated valves and pipe flanges where: - valves are in frequent use and/or are of the packed gland type; - flange joints may be broken whilst the plant is not in a gas free condition; - the space is continuously ventilated except when the plant is in a gas free condition. - loss of ventilation is alarmed at a manned station. (iii) Areas on open deck within 3 m of cargo/storage tank ventilation outlets which permit the flow of small volumes of vapour caused by thermal variation.		(i) Equipment/cables as permitted in Hazard Category C. (ii) Flameproof - Ex 'd'. (iii) Increased safety-Ex 'c' except motors (iv) Pressurised - Ex 'p'. (v) Other electrical equipment specially approved for use in Zone 1 and acceptable to the Appropriate Authority. (vi) Through runs of cable.

D continued on

P (140)

39

Table 23.2 cont (Modified P (141))

Hazard Category	Description of Location	Typical Example	Permitted Certified Safe type Equipment/Cables
E	(i) Areas on open deck within 3 m of process plant.		(i) Equipment/cables permitted in Hazard Category D.
	(ii) Areas on open deck within 3 m of: - valves which are infrequently used: - flange joints which are broken only when the ship is in a gas free condition.		(ii) Equipment of a type which ensures the absence of sparks or arcs and absence of ignition capable surfaces during its normal operation and acceptable to the Approprite Authority.
	(iii) Enclosed and semi-enclosed spaces with closed process plant and associated valves and pipe flanges where: - valves are infrequently used: - flange joints are only broken when the plant is in a gas free condition: - the space is continuously ventilated except when the plant is in a gas free condition and loss of ventilation is alarmed at a normally manned station. Note: Open sample points should be subject to special consideration.	process plant	(iii) Equipment specifically designed for use in Zone 2 and acceptable to the Appropriate Authority.
	(iv) Enclosed and semi-enclosed spaces in which pipes containing cargo are located and which have continuous mechanical ventilation except when the pipes are in a gas free condition and loss of ventilation is alarmed at a manned station.		
	(v) Areas on open deck within 3 m of openings in spaces of Hazard Category E.		

Note: The action to be taken on loss of ventilation should be incorporated in formal operating instructions. Such instructions are outside the scope of these Recommendations.

Section 24

P(143), Clause 24.2; replace by:

24.2   System earthing and protection

System earthing and the detection of system insulation defects should be arranged in accordance with 2.1(*).

P(146), Sub-Clause 24.6(3); add the following note:

NOTE: BS 587 is obsolescent.

Section 25

P(150), Sub-Clause 25.7(1)(iv); replace by:

(iv)   An indicator for each propeller shaft at each control station to show speed, direction and pitch, as appropriate.

P(151), Sub-Clause 25.7(2)(iv); replace by:

(iv)   An indicator for each propeller shaft at each control station to show speed, direction and pitch, as appropriate.

Section 26

P(156), Clause 26.1; add a note below the heading to read:

NOTE: Attention is drawn to the requirements of Section 21(*), in so far as they are applicable.

P(157), Sub-Clause 26.2(7); replace by:

(7)   Systems should be arranged to minimise common mode failure, *i.e.* multiple failures attributable to a common cause.

Section 27

P(162) to P(166); replace completely with the revised text given in pages 42 to 49 inclusive.

TESTS AND INSPECTIONS OF COMPLETED INSTALLATIONS

27.1   Before new installations, or alterations of or additions to an existing installation, are put into service the appropriate inspections and tests specified in 27.2 to 27.7 inclusive, should be made. Such tests should be in addition to, and not in substitution for, the acceptance tests of the individual items of plant at the maker's works.

These inspections and tests are intended to indicate the general condition of the installation at the time of completion and form part of the assessment of the acceptable condition of the installation. They do not in themselves necessarily ensure that the installation is satisfactory in all respects. The test methods and their results should be recorded to assist with subsequent and periodic assessment of the condition of the installation.

Tests which simulate conditions to establish the integrity of the apparatus and circuits may be used provided that the effect is the same as the specified tests and/or conditions.

During the life of an installation, it is necessary to systematically inspect and test its apparatus and circuits to ensure that it is maintained in a sound condition and any undue deterioration that may have taken place can be detected. Whereas the initial tests are to demonstrate that the system has been designed and installed in an acceptable manner, the subsequent tests and inspections are to demonstrate that the equipment has not deteriorated. These tests may not necessarily be as stringent or the same as those conducted initially. The frequency of the periodic checks will depend upon the type of installation, experience obtained from previous checks and any Statutory or similar requirements.

All defects thus discovered should be made good as soon as possible.

Care should always be taken when carrying out tests on apparatus and circuits to ensure that no adverse effects are experienced by any persons in the vicinity of the apparatus or circuits being tested or by other equipment or parts of the system or systems.

This is especially relevant where circuits are in or pass through hazardous areas.

27.2   Insulation resistance

(1)   The insulation resistance should be measured, preferably by self-contained instruments such as a direct-reading insulation resistance tester applying an appropriate voltage.

This voltage should be d.c. at the test values shown in Table 27.1 or as recommended in the relevant British Standard.

Table 27.1

Nominal voltage d.c. or a.c. r.m.s. 1	Test voltage d.c. 2
V	V
Up to 500	500
Above 500 to 1000	1000
Above 1000 to 6000	2500
Above 6000 to 15000	5000

NOTE: Care should be taken on equipment operating below 60 V and on semiconductor devices to ensure that no damage is sustained due to the application of excessive test voltages.

When an insulation test is made on a circuit incorporating capacitors of a total capacitance exceeding 2 microfarads, an insulation tester of the constant-voltage type should be used in order to ensure that accurate test readings are obtained.

The periodic testing of insulation resistance throughout the life of the installation and comparison with previously recorded test results will assist with detecting deterioration in the condition of a circuit or apparatus.

(2)   A test for insulation resistance should be applied to all permanent wiring of communications, lighting and power circuits between all insulated poles and earth and, where practicable, between poles. The installation may be sub-divided to any desired extent and appliances may be disconnected if tests give results lower than those in Table 27.2.

Table 27.2

Nominal voltage of circuit 1	Minimum insulation resistance 2
V Below 50 50 to 440 Greater than 440	Megohms 0.3 1.0 $\dfrac{\text{Nominal Voltage}}{1000} + 1.0$

NOTE: Attention is drawn to the importance of recording the temperature of windings of rotating machines at the same time as the insulation resistance. The insulation resistance of machine windings varies considerably with temperature. Corrected values may be obtained by reference to Figure 27.1.

27.3   High Voltage Tests

Equipment rated at or above 1 kV and assembled on site should be subjected to a high voltage dielectric test after assembly. Test voltages should be those recommended for site conditions given in the relevant British Standard.

Cables operating at or above 1 kV a.c. should be subjected to a high voltage dielectric test after terminations have been completed. These tests should be made prior to connection to the apparatus unless links are provided to allow isolation of the cable from the apparatus. The test voltage should be d.c. at 4 times the rated voltage for a duration of 15 minutes.

Where it is not possible to separate the cable(s) from the equipment for the test, a test voltage and duration, appropriate to the type of equipment to which the cables are connected, should be applied.

High voltage tests can weaken the dielectric materials and should, therefore, only be carried out at the time of initial installation. Any subsequent tests following additions, modifications or repairs should be applied with caution and then only at reduced voltages as recommended by the relevant British Standard.

The above tests should always be preceded and followed by an insulation resistance test.

27.4   Earth continuity

(1)   Tests should be made to verify that all earth continuity conductors and earthing leads are connected to the frame of apparatus and to the hull of metal ships or the main earth conductor bar of ships with non-metallic hulls and that socket-outlet earthing terminals are connected to earth. This should also apply where apparatus is bonded directly to the hull.

The earthing arrangements of some control, instrumentation and/or intrinsically safe systems may differ from the normal power earth arrangements and should be given special consideration, *e.g.* low voltage/low current test equipment.

(2)   Where metal-sheathed cables are used, whether armoured or not, tests should be made to verify that all metallic envelopes are electrically continuous throughout their length and are earthed as required by Sections 2(*), 11(*) and 24(*), or as may be required for particular arrangements such as when they form part of a control, instrument or intrinsically safe system.

(3)   Where earthed systems are used, it should be verified that:

(i)   Single-pole control devices and fuses are connected in the live conductor only. (It should be noted that double-pole isolation is required for installations in hazardous areas.)

(ii)   Wiring has been connected correctly to plugs and sockets.

(iii)   The outer contacts of Edison screw-type lampholders are connected to the earthed conductor.

27.5   Earth fault loop impedance

Where protective measures are used which require a knowledge of earth fault loop impedance, the relevant impedances should be measured, or determined by an equally effective method.

Tests should be made at the completion of the installation and be re-assessed at periodic intervals, but care should be taken on installations in hazardous areas, as mentioned in 27.6.

27.6   Tests on installations in hazardous areas

(1)   Where tests involve equipment that is situated in or circuits that pass through a hazardous area, care should be taken that the tests required by 27.2 to 27.5 do not cause incendive arcs, sparks or hot surfaces.

(2)   The testing of the installation prior to the introduction of the potentially hazardous materials may be carried out using normal methods but subsequent testing may require alternative techniques, see BS 5345, Part 1.

(3)   Care should also be exercised with the use of intrinsically safe test instruments as, under certain conditions, they could result in the production of incendive sparks.

(4)   Care should be taken when testing to ensure that intrinsically safe systems and their earthing arrangements are not violated.

27.7   Performance Tests

(1)   All switchgear should be loaded as nearly as practicable to its working load in order to demonstrate that no overheating takes place due to faulty connections or incorrect rating.

Infra-red photometry techniques may be employed to assist with this assessment. The measurement of the resistance of joints and contacts by volt drop methods with the injection of high current from a low voltage source is also recommended. Records should be taken of the readings for subsequent reference.

These techniques may be used at the initial examination and for periodic inspections.

Switches and circuit-breakers should be operated on load and the satisfactory operation of all interlocks is to be demonstrated.

Prior to commencing tests of protective devices, their size, type and ratings should be checked against the design. The operation of protective relays and devices should be effectively demonstrated, which may be by the use of suitable injection testing techniques. Direct acting overcurrent relays can only be tested by primary injection methods but secondary injection may be acceptable elsewhere when the associated current transformers and circuitry should also be tested.

(2)   All generator sets should be run over a sufficient range of load, including full rated load, or as near as is practicable to full rated load, and for a duration sufficient to demonstrate that commutation, electrical characteristics, governing, range of excitation control, phase rotation, lubrication and absence of excessive vibration are satisfactory.

If sets are intended to operate in parallel, they should be tested over a range of loads to demonstrate their compliance with 9.4(3) or 9.18, as appropriate.

The voltage and speed regulation when a specified load is suddenly thrown on and off should be satisfactory to previously defined limits. See 9.4 and Section 25(*).

Overspeed trips together with all other devices relative to the protection of the generator sets should be demonstrated to show that they are satisfactory.

Synchronising equipment and any associated protective devices should be demonstrated to verify correct functioning between each generating set and all other generating sets intended to operate in parallel. Reverse current, reverse power and overcurrent trips and any other safety devices should be satisfactorily demonstrated.

(3)   Each motor, together with its control gear, should be tested to prove the wiring and direction of rotation and then run as near as practicable to service conditions for a sufficient length of time to demonstrate that alignment, speed range, commutation, rated output and operating characteristics are satisfactory.

(4)   All electrical devices and circuits, including lighting, heating and galley equipment, should be tested under operating conditions to verify that they are suitable and satisfactory for their purposes.

(5)   Each communications system and alarm system should be thoroughly tested to determine its suitability and to verify its specified functioning.

(6)   Equipment installed to implement relevant Statutory requirements should be tested to ensure that all such requirements have been met. Where operation is required to be maintained from emergency sources of power, including automatic transfer of circuits to such emergency sources, correct functioning from and by such emergency supplies should be tested and the duration of the emergency supplies, where specified, should also be verified.

(7)   All equipment, including radio communication equipment, radio naviga-tion aids, depth-sounding and broadcasting apparatus, should be tested for the purpose of detecting harmful interference. If objectionable interference is found, it should be reduced by suitable means to the level prescribed in BS 1597.

(8)   Batteries should be subjected to an initial test to demonstrate their ability to supply their design loads for the duration required. The associated charging system for each battery should also be verified.

> NOTE: Regular testing to demonstrate this capability should be carried out in accordance with the manufacturer's recommended procedures.

(9)   The ventilation arrangements of vented type battery installations should be inspected to ensure that they are in accordance with 14.11(*); the arrangements for valve regulated sealed battery installations should comply with 14.16(*). Ventilation air flow should be tested to confirm that at least the minimum quantity is obtained.

(10)   Attention is drawn to the special tests for propulsion equipment which are detailed in 25.10.

27.8   The appropriate ratings of fuses and the settings of adjustable protection devices and the full load current of the generator or cables protected should be indicated.

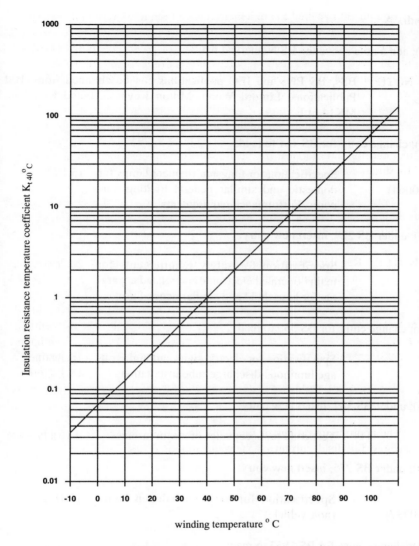

To convert observed insulation resistance (R_t) to 40°C multiply by temperature coefficient $K_{t\,40\,°C}$. $R_{40\,°C} = R_t \times K_{t\,40\,°C}$

Figure 27.1   Recommended practice for testing insulation resistance of rotating machinery. Reference IEEE Standard 43-1974.

Appendix A

P(173); add a note above the BS Numerical list:

NOTE: BSs, BS ENs and IEC publications can be obtained from: BSI Publications, Linford Wood, Milton Keynes, United Kingdom, MK14 6LE.

P(173); change entry for BS 161 to read:

161 (EN 60064)	Specification for tungsten filament lamps for domestic and similar general lighting purposes. Performance requirements	15.1 (*)

P(173); under BS 229, insert new entry:

415	Specification for safety requirements for mains-operated electronic and related apparatus for household and similar general use	20.2(*)

P(174); change entry for BS 559 to read:

559	Specification for electric signs and high-voltage luminous-discharge-tube installations	15.18(*) 18.1, Note1

P(174); under BS 587, insert new entry:

752	Test code for acceptance of steam turbines	9.1(i)(*)

P(174); under BS 775, insert new entry:

1075 (EN 60357)	Specification for tungsten halogen lamps (non-vehicle)	15.1(*)

P(174); change entry for BS 1853 to read:

1853 Pt. 1 (EN 60081)	Tubular fluorescent lamps for general lighting service. Specification for internationally specified lamps	15.1(*)

| 1853 Pt. 2 | Specification for lamps used in the United Kingdom not included in Part 1 | |

P(174); change entry for BS 2818 to read:

| 2818 | Withdrawn, replaced by BS EN 60920 and BS EN 60921 | 15.15(*) |

P(174); delete entry for BS 3052.

P(175); for BS 3535 entry (Clause column),   add   19.4(10)(*), 19.4(11)(*).

P(175); change entry for BS 3677 to read:

| 3677 (EN 60188) | Specification for high pressure mercury vapour lamps | 15.1(*) |

P(175); under BS 3677, insert new entry;

| 3767 | Specification for low pressure sodium vapour lamps | 15.1(*) |

P(175); change entry for BS 3772 to read:

| 3772 (EN 60155) | Specification for starters for fluorescent lamps | 15.15(*) |

P(175); change entry for BS 4017 to read:

| 4017 | No longer used. See BS EN 61048 and BS EN 61049. | 15.15(*) |

P(176); for BS 4533 add (EN 60598)

P(176); change entry for BS 4782 to read:

| 4782 | Withdrawn, replaced by BS EN 60922 and BS EN 60923 | 15.15(*) |

P(177); under BS 5655, insert new entry:

5784	Safety of electrical commercial catering equipment	16.1(*)

P(177); under BS 5907, insert two new entries:

5932	Specification for sealed nickel-cadmium cylindrical rechargeable single cells	14.15(*)
5968	Methods of acceptance testing of industrial type steam turbines	9.1(i)(*)

P(177); change entry for BS 5971 to read:

5971 (EN 60432)	Specification for safety of tungsten filament lamps for domestic and similar general lighting purposes	15.(1)(*)

P(178); under BS 6141, insert new entry:

6193 (EN 60662)	Specification for high pressure sodium vapour lamps	15.1(*)

P(178); change entry for BS 6702 to read:

6702	Withdrawn, replaced by BS EN 60400.	15.3(*)

P(178); under BS 6724, insert new entry:

6745	Portable lead-acid cells and batteries	14.15(*)
Part 1	Specification for performance, design and construction of valve regulated sealed type	

P(179); under BS 6746, insert new entry:

6776 (EN 60238)	Specification for Edison screw lampholder	15.2(1)(*)

P(179); change the entry for BS 6883 to read:

6883	Specification for elastomer insulated cables for fixed wiring in ships and on mobile and fixed offshore units	6.4(*), 10.2(*), 10.3(*), Table 10.1(*), 11.17 (8)(*), 11.17 (14)(*).

P(179); under BS 6977, insert new entry:

6982 (EN 60901)	Single-capped fluorescent lamps. Safety and performance requirements	15.1(*)

P(179); under BS 7027, insert three new entries and a listing of BS ENs:

7211	Thermosetting insulated cables (non-armoured) for electric power and lighting with low emission of smoke and corrosive gases when affected by fire	6.4(*), 10.2(*), 11.17 (8)(*).
7609	Code of practice for installation and inspection of uninsulated compression and mechanical connectors for power cables with copper or aluminium conductors	11.12(1)(*)
MA2 Part 3	Magnetic compasses and binnacles	1.29(1)(*)

BS ENs

EN 60400	Specification for lampholders for tubular fluorescent lamps and starterholders	15.3(*)
EN 60920	Specification for ballasts for tubular fluorescent lamps. General and safety requirements	15.15(*)
EN 60921	Specification for ballasts for tubular fluorescent lamps. Performance requirements	15.15(*)

EN 60922	Specification for general and safety requirements for ballasts for discharge lamps (excluding tubular fluorescent lamps)	15.15(*)
EN 60923	Specification for performance requirements for ballasts for discharge lamps (excluding tubular fluorescent lamps	15.15(*)
EN 60924	Specification for general and safety requirements for d.c. supplied electronic ballasts for tubular fluorescent lamps	15.15(*)
EN 60925	Specification for performance requirements for d.c. supplied electronic ballasts for tubular fluorescent lamps	15.15(*)
EN 60926	Specification for general and safety requirements for starting devices (other than glow starters)	15.15(*)
EN 60927	Specification for performance requirements for starting devices (other than glow starters)	15.15(*)
EN 60928	Specification for a.c. supplied electronic ballasts for tubular fluorescent lamps. General and safety requirements	15.15(*)
EN 60929	Specification for a.c. supplied electronic ballasts for tubular fluorescent lamps. Performance requirements	15.15(*)
EN 60968	Specification for self-ballasted lamps for general lighting services. Safety requirements	15.1(*)
EN 60969	Specification for self-ballasted lamps for general lighting services. Performance requirements.	15.1(*)

EN 61046	Specification for d.c. or a.c. supplied electronic step-down convertors for filament lamps. General and safety requirements	15.15(*)
EN 61047	Specification for d.c. or a.c. supplied electronic step-down convertors for filament lamps. Performance requirements	15.15(*)
EN 61048	Specification for capacitors for use in tubular fluorescent and other discharge lamp circuits. General and safety requirements	15.15(*)
EN 61049	Specification for capacitors for use in tubular fluorescent and other discharge lamp circuits. Performance requirements	15.15(*)
EN 61050	Specification for transformers for tubular discharge lamps having a no-load output voltage exceeding 1000 V (generally called neon-transformers). General and safety requirements	15.18(*)

P(179); under IEC 34-1, insert new entry:

38	IEC standard voltages	Section 11, Appendix (*)

P(180); under IEC 955, insert new entry:

1184	Bayonet lampholders	15.2(1)(*)

Appendix C

P(188), Sub-Clause C.1(3); amend the YARD address to:

BA^{e}SEMA,
1 Atlantic Quay,
Broomielaw,
Glasgow,
United Kingdom,
G2 8JE.
(Formerly YARD)

Also delete the "A" in the report reference number.

P(195), Sub-Clause C.3.4(5); delete the entire NOTE.

Appendix D

P(198), Clause D.1; amend the YARD address as in the amendment for P(188) above.

P(199), Clause D.2, last paragraph, third sentence; delete:

... they tend to be used in a different way, and ...

P(203), Sub-Clause D.4(4)(v); delete the paragraph number "(v)" but leave the text to form a second paragraph to Sub-Clause D.4(4)(iv). Also renumber Sub-Clause D.4(4)(vi) as D.4(4)(v).

P(205), Sub-Clause D.4(6)(ix); replace by:

(ix)   Spare cores.

Where unused cores exist in multi-cable runs or within multicore cables, they should normally be isolated and taped back at each end. Alternatively, it may be possible to achieve a better EMC environment by connecting them in parallel with cores already in use. Earthing of unused cores at one or both ends is not normally advisable but may be appropriate in particular cases.

P(206), Sub-Clause D.4(7)(iv); replace by:

(iv)   Fibre optic cable techniques and optical isolators are available to meet a broad range of applications. Their use should, therefore, be considered when solving EMC problems but "tailor-made" applications may be required to meet individual situations.

P(206), Clause D.5, paragraph 2; change

"1980" to "1992".

Also replace the last two paragraphs of Sub-Clause D.5(1) by the following:

Careful consideration should be given to long wire ropes and stays which if earthed at one end form effective antennas which will absorb and re-radiate RF energy.

Where practicable, such wire ropes and stays should be divided by the use of insulators into a number of non-resonant sections of varying lengths not exceeding 5m. The top and bottom insulators should be positioned so that they are beyond the normal reach of personnel. The top and lowest lengths of a divided wire rope or stay should be electrically bonded to an adjacent earthed part of the superstructure. See also BS 1597 and BS 5260.

P(208), Sub-Clause D.5(5); delete final paragraph.

APPENDIX 1

Errata Applicable to the 1990, Sixth Edition

P(v)   amend title of the Committee to
"SHIPS and OFFSHORE INSTALLATIONS COMMITTEE".
See also pages vi and vii of this Supplement for information on the
Constitution of the Committee.

PART THREE

Section 1

P(7), Clause 1.36, line 1: delete the "comma" after "1.7".

Section 6

P(23), Sub-Clause 6.6(1), line 1: change "principle" to "principal".

Section 12

P(71), Table 12.3, column 6: amend "8.3" to "2.3".

P(78), Table 12.10, column 9: amend "mV" to "A" and, in column 10, amend "A" to "mV".

P(84), Table 12.16, 2nd line: after "PVC" change "without" to "with".

Appendix C

P(188), Sub-Clause C.2, line 5: change "artefact" to "artifice".

P(192), Sub-Clause C.3.3(4), line 6: change "police" to "pole".

P(195), Sub-Clause C.4.2(6), line 2: change "possibly" to "possible".

P(197), Sub-Clause C.5.2(3)(ii), line 4: change "facing" to "fault".

Appendix D

P(198), Clause D.1, penultimate line: amend "BS 7207" to "BS 7027".

P(198) to P(208) inclusive: amend "antennae" to "antennas" wherever the former appears.

P(199), Sub-Clause D.3(1)(i), line 1: change "on" to "in".

APPENDIX 2

List of Alterations and Additions to the 1990, Sixth Edition

This Appendix summarises those Clauses and Sub-Clauses within the Sixth Edition which are affected by the amendments included in this Supplement and the Errata listed in Appendix 1 to this Supplement. Where the amendments affect a cross-reference contained in such Clauses and Sub-Clauses, the relevant cross-reference is additionally identified by *italic* type.

P(*v*),   Committee Title.

PART 2

P(*xiii*) to P(*xix*),   complete new part.

PART 3

Section 1

P(5),	Clause 1.18.
P(6),	Clause 1.29.
P(7),	Clause 1.36.

Section 2

P(9) to P(14),   complete new Section.

Section 4

P(20),   Clause 4.6.

Section 6

P(23),	Clause 6.4 and Sub-Clause 6.6(1).
P(26),	Sub-Clause 6.11(1).

Section 7

P(29),	Clause 7.6.
P(31),	Sub-Clause 7.7(5)(i).
P(32),	Sub-Clause 7.8(7).

Section 8

P(40),	Clause 8.12 and Sub-Clause 8.13(2).

Section 9

P(41),	Clause 9.1.
P(43),	Clause 9.10.
P(44),	Clause 9.14; Clause 9.15, line 2; *1.18*; Clause 9.19.
P(46),	Sub-Clause 9.23(3), line 2; *9.19*.

Section 10

P(48),   Sub-Clause 10.1(3), line 2; *Section 2*; Sub-Clause 10.1(4)(ii); Sub-Clause 10.1(6).

P(49),   Sub-Clause 10.1(7); Sub-Clause 10.1(8); see also new Sub-Clauses 10.1(9) and 10.1(10); Clause 10.2.

P(50),   Clause 10.3; Clause 10.4, line 2; *11.17*; Clause 10.5; see also new Table 10.1.

P(51),   Table 10.1.

Section 11

P(52),   Clause 11.1; Sub-Clause 11.2(1).

P(62),   Sub-Clauses 11.12(1) and 11.12(5).

P(64),   Clause 11.15; see also new Sub-Clause 11.15(7).

P(65),   Sub-Clauses 11.17(4) and 11.17(5).

| P(66), | Sub-Clauses 11.17(8) and 11.17(9); see also new Sub-Clauses 11.17(13) and 11.17(14) and new Appendix. |

Section 12

P(71),	Table 12.3.
P(78),	Table 12.10.
P(84),	Table 12.16.

Section 13

| P(88), | Clause 13.1. |
| P(90), | Clause 13.10. |

Section 14

| P(91) to P(96), | complete new Section. |

Section 15

P(97),	Clause 15.1 and Sub-Clause 15.2(1).
P(98),	Sub-Clause 15.2(5), Table 15.2 and Clause 15.3
P(100),	Clauses 15.15 and 15.16.
P(101),	Clause 15.18.

Section 16

| P(102), | Clauses 16.1 and 16.9. |

Section 19

| P(110), | Sub-Clause 19.3(3). |
| P(111), | Sub-Clauses 19.4(10) and 19.4(11). |

Section 20

| P(113), | Clause 20.2. |

Section 21

| P(115), | Sub-Clause 21.2(3). |

Section 23

P(128),	Sub-Clause 23.2(1)(i).
P(139) and P(141),	Table 23.2.

Section 24

P(143),	Clause 24.2.
P(146),	Sub-Clause 24.6(3).

Section 25

P(150),	Sub-Clause 25.7(1)(iv).
P(151),	Sub-Clause 25.7(2)(iv).

Section 26

P(156),	Clause 26.1.
P(157),	Sub-Clause 26.2(7).

Section 27

P(162) to P(166),	complete new Section.

Appendix A

P(173) to P(179),	numerous changes and additions to the listed British Standards.
P(179) and P(180),	two IEC Standards added.

Appendix C

P(188),	Sub-Clause C.2.
P(192),	Sub-Clause C.3.3(4).
P(195),	Sub-Clause C.4.2(6).
P(197),	Sub-Clause C.5.2(3)(ii).

Appendix D

P(198),	Clause D.1.
P(198) to P(208),	numerous changes to "antennae".
P(199),	Sub-Clause D.3(1)(i).